For all portable keyboards *by Kenneth Baker.*

THE COMPLETE
ROCK & POP
KEYBOARD PLAYER
BOOK 1

Wise Publications
London/New York/Sydney/Cologne

Exclusive Distributors:

Music Sales Limited
8/9 Frith Street, London W1V 5TZ, England.

Music Sales Pty. Limited
120 Rothschild Avenue, Rosebery, NSW 2018, Australia.

This book © Copyright 1986 by Wise Publications.
ISBN 0.7119.0884.2
Order No. AM 62688

Art direction by Mike Bell.
Designed by Bamber Forsyth Design.
Cover design by Pearce Marchbank.
Arranged by Kenneth Baker.

Music Sales complete catalogue lists thousands of
titles and is free from your local music book shop, or direct
from Music Sales Limited.
Please send £1 in stamps for postage to
Music Sales Limited, 8/9 Frith Street, London W1V 5TZ.

Printed in England by
J.B. Offset Printers (Marks Tey) Limited, Marks Tey.

ABOUT THESE BOOKS

The Complete Rock & Pop Keyboard Player is for all student keyboard players who like good pop music.

The Course features eighteen top groups and solo artists (six in each book). Three songs have been chosen for each artist: there are famous hit songs, songs that are particularly representative of the artist, or simply songs that come off well on an electronic keyboard.

Book One of the Course continues on from Books 1, 2 and 3 of 'The Complete Keyboard Player' (the standard books). In these books you learnt how to use the modern portable electronic keyboard, and how to read music. Using popular standard tunes you learnt basic keyboard techniques, including how to finger correctly, how to play left hand chords, how to play rhythmically.

YOU MUST MASTER THESE EARLY STEPS BEFORE BEGINNING BOOK ONE OF THE PRESENT COURSE.

Whilst the Course is meant to be progressive as it stands, feel free to jump ahead sometimes, or to leave out certain songs, if it suits your particular needs.

Although I have tried to match each written song with the original recording as far as practicable, I found it necessary sometimes to shorten the originals, in order to save awkward page turns. I have also simplified the phrasing of the melodies at times, in order to make reading easier for you. Play along with the original recording if you can, to get the true feeling of the song. I have written mostly in the same key as the record. Where the keys are not the same, use the 'transposer' on your keyboard to compensate.

Look out for the 'double-tracking' songs (there are three or four in each book). You will learn a lot by playing with a pre-recorded track. It will teach you counting and timing as nothing else will, but you may have to persevere to get it right. If you find when laying down your first track that you run out of recording 'space' on your keyboard, leave out a repeat or two.

Whatever you do, have fun!

George Benson

Ultravox

Phil Collins

Chris De Burgh

Culture Club

Eurythmics

CONTENTS

FOR ROSANNA

Words & Music by Chris de Burgh

Suggested registration: flute
Rhythm: rock
Tempo: fairly slow (♩ = 80)

VERSES

1. This is for Ro - san - na, sweet girl of mine. _____
(2.) sleep - ing in here to - night. _____
(3.) grow - ing from baby to child, _____

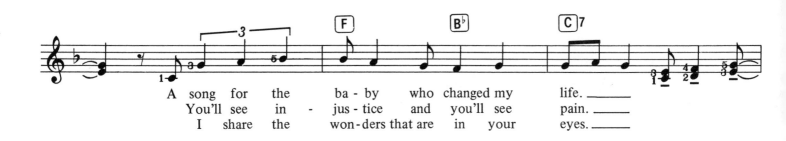

A song for the ba - by who changed my life. _____
You'll see in - jus - tice and you'll see pain. _____
I share the won - ders that are in your eyes. _____

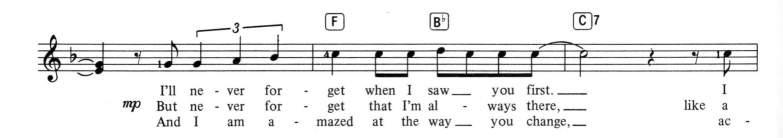

I'll ne - ver for - get when I saw _ you first. _____ I
But ne - ver for - get that I'm al - ways there, _ like a
And I am a - mazed at the way _ you change, _ ac -

thought that my heart would burst with the love _ that I have.
sha - dow _ by your side, with the love _ that I have.
cord - ding to the plan, and the love _ that I have.

1.
2. As I watch you

2.

INTERLUDE

flute to oboe

Oh, how _ my heart _ it _ is shin - ing, oh, how _ my heart _

6

___ it is shin - ing. Oh, how_ this heart, it is shin - ing __ through, ___

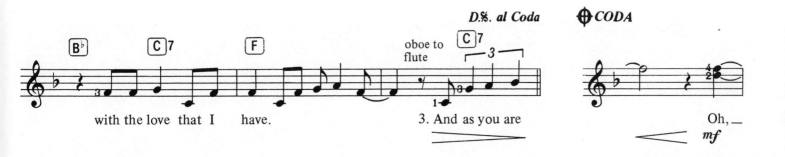

D.%. al Coda   ⊕ **CODA**

oboe to flute

with the love that I have.   3. And as you are   Oh, __

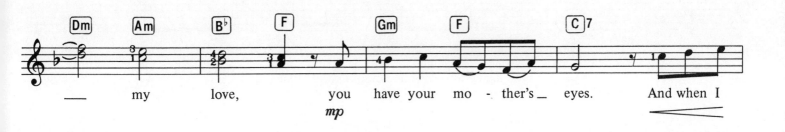

___ my love, you have your mo - ther's _ eyes.   And when I_

see you laugh, you have your mo - ther's smile, __ and you are __

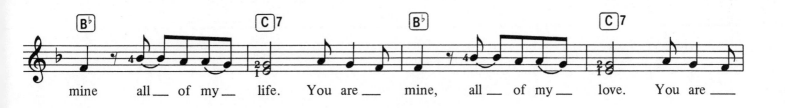

mine all_ of my_ life. You are __ mine, all_ of my_ love. You are __

mine, blood_ of my_ blood, you are __ mine.

FATAL HESITATION

Words & Music by Chris de Burgh

Suggested registration: guitar
Rhythm: rock
Tempo: medium ($\quarternote$ = 100)

1. The ca - fés __ are all de - ser - ted, the streets are wet a - gain. __
ne - ver gon-na love an - o - ther, the way that I've loved you. __
saw you __ a - gain this morn - ing, walk - ing down the beach..

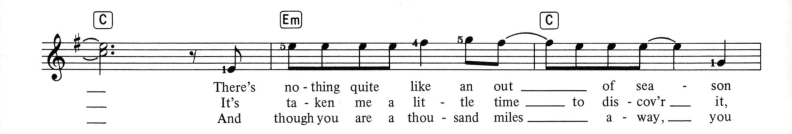

__ There's no - thing quite like an out __ of sea - son
__ It's ta - ken me a lit - tle time __ to dis - cov'r __ it,
__ And though you are a thou - sand miles __ a - way, __ you

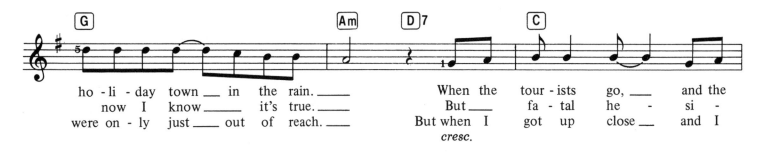

ho - li - day town __ in the rain. __ When the tour - ists go, __ and the
now I know __ it's true. __ But __ fa - tal he - si -
were on - ly just __ out of reach. __ But when I got up close __ and I

cresc.

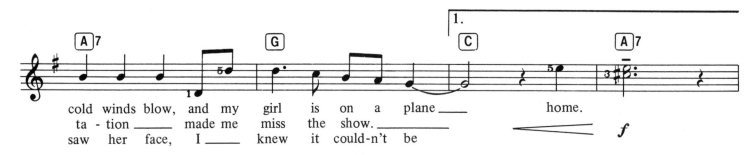

1.

cold winds blow, and my girl is on a plane __ home.
ta - tion __ made me miss the show. __
saw her face, I __ knew it could-n't be

f

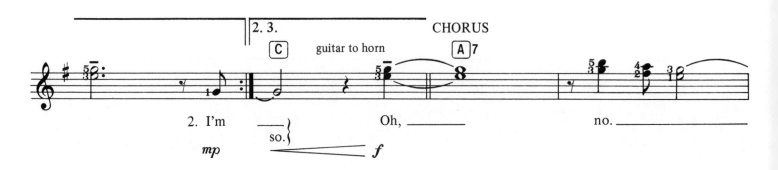

2. 3.

CHORUS

guitar to horn

2. I'm __ } Oh, __ no. __
so. }

mp   *f*

8

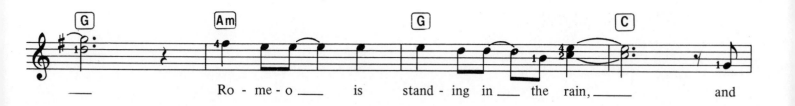

Ro - me - o ___ is stand - ing in ___ the rain, ___ and

I know ___ that I ___ have let her slip a - way.

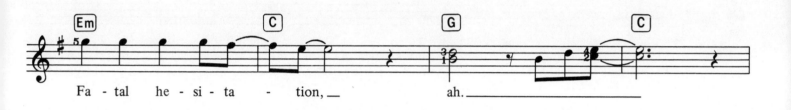

Fa - tal he - si - ta - tion, ___ ah. ___

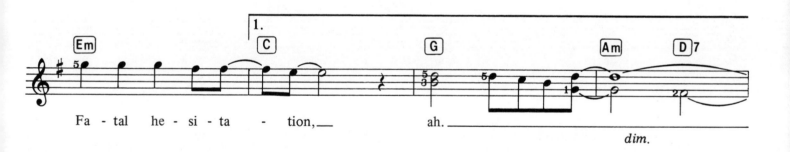

Fa - tal he - si - ta - tion, ___ ah. ___

dim.

horn to guitar

3. I ___ tion.   I'm gon - na get on my ___

mp   *mf*

(Repeat and Fade)

___ boat,   and sail a - way. ___

ONE WORD (STRAIGHT TO THE HEART)

Words & Music by Chris de Burgh

Suggested registration: string ensemble
Rhythm: rock
Tempo: medium ($\quarternote$ = 120)

VERSES

1. Mid-night, and all is well, ___ I hear the mis-sion bell. ___
2. Head-lights are blaz-ing through, ___ turn on the radio I hear the news. ___

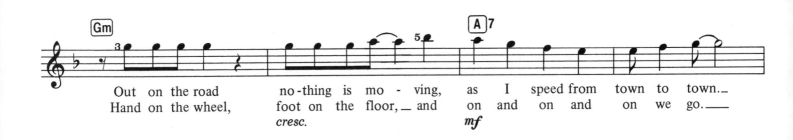

Out on the road no-thing is mo-ving, as I speed from town to town. ___
Hand on the wheel, foot on the floor, ___ and on and on and on we go. ___

cresc. *mf*

Two hearts are beat-ing fast, ___ but they are still ___ ma-ny
This car is like a friend, ___ bring her the mes-sage that I

mp

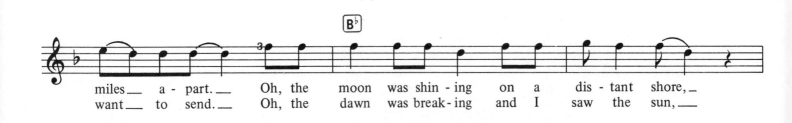

miles ___ a - part. ___ Oh, the moon was shin-ing on a dis-tant shore, ___
want ___ to send. ___ Oh, the dawn was break-ing and I saw the sun, ___

burn-ing like a fire in my heart. ___ I've got to see her, ___ I've got to
burn-ing like a fire on the bay. ___ I'm near-ly there now, ___ I'm gon-na

cresc. *mf*

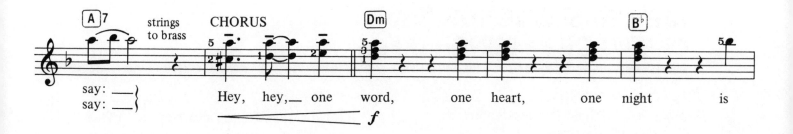

say: ———}
say: ———}

Hey, hey,— one word, one heart, one night is

all — I want._One word, one heart, one girl is wait-ing there_ for

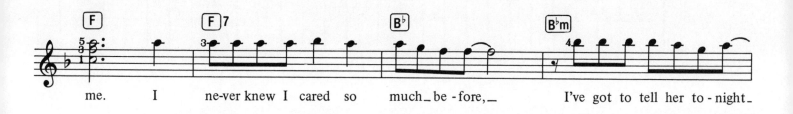

me. I ne-ver knew I cared so much_be-fore,_ I've got to tell her to-night_

— (straight to the heart_) I'm gon-na tell her to-night._ (straight to the heart_

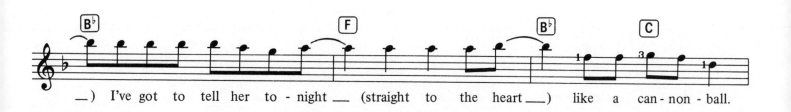

—) I've got to tell her to-night _ (straight to the heart_) like a can-non-ball.

CHORD OF B MINOR (Bm); CHORD OF F♯ MINOR (F♯m)

1

You will need these two new chords in 'Changing Every Day', on p.16.

Using single-finger chord method:

Locate 'B' and 'F♯' (the lower one) in the accompaniment section of your keyboard.

Convert these notes into 'Bm' and 'F♯m' respectively (see The Complete Keyboard Player, Book Two, p.28, and your owner's manual).

Using fingered chord method:

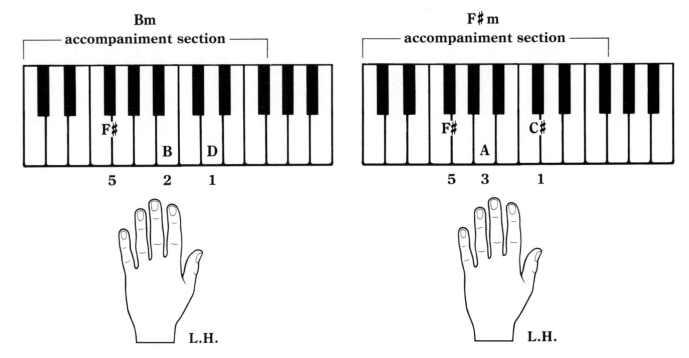

CHURCH OF THE POISON MIND

Words & Music by Culture Club

Suggested registration: organ – saxophone – tremolo
Rhythm: rock
Tempo: medium (♩ = 126)

VERSES

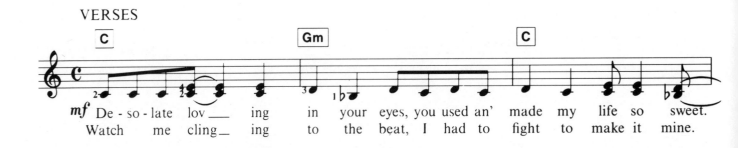

mf De - so - late lov___ ing in your eyes, you used an' made my life so sweet.
Watch me cling___ ing to the beat, I had to fight to make it mine.

Step out like___ a God - found child, I saw your
That re - lig - ion you could sink it neat, just move your

KARMA CHAMELEON

Words & Music by O'Dowd, Moss, Hay, Craig & Pickett

Suggested registration: synthe + music box
(or piano). Duet, if available
Rhythm: rock
Tempo: fast (♩ = 168)
synchro-start, if available

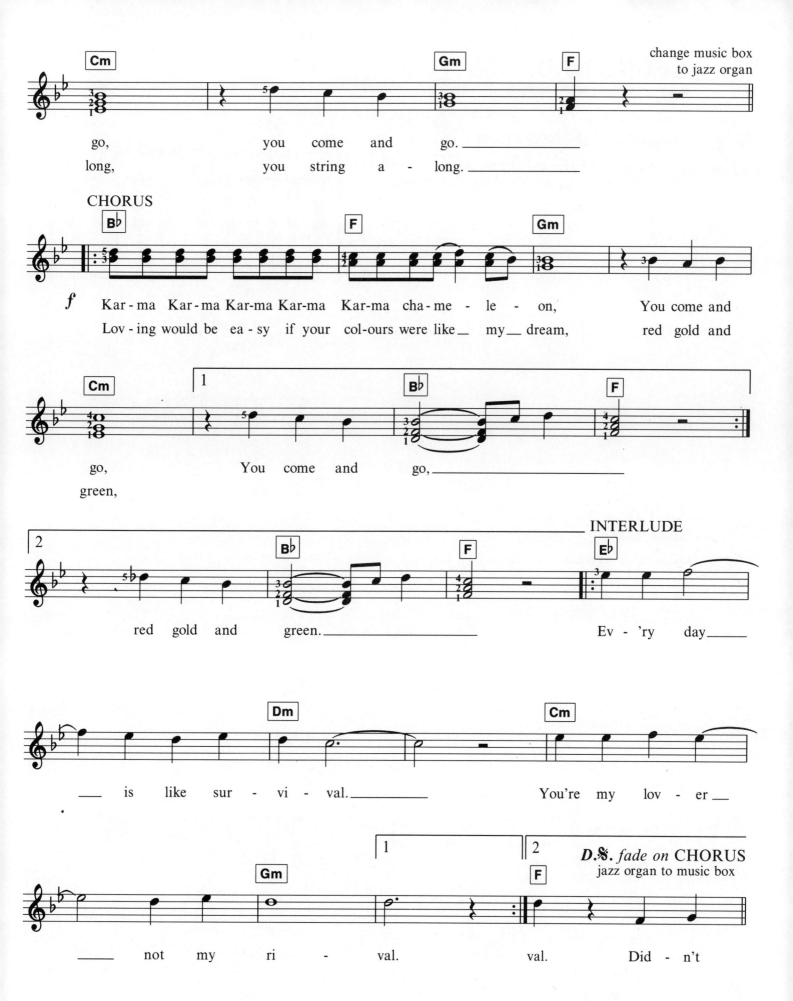

CHORD OF D

2

Using single-finger chord method:

Play the note 'D' (the higher one of two) in the accompaniment section of your keyboard.

Using fingered chord method:

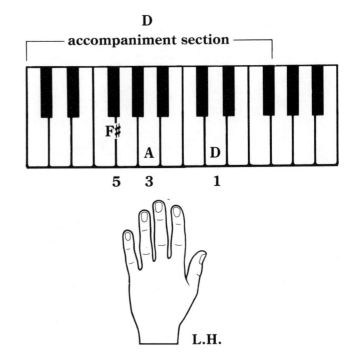

CHANGING EVERY DAY

Words & Music by Culture Club

Suggested registration: piano + trombone + chorus (chorale)
Rhythm: rock
Tempo: quite fast (♩ = 152)
synchro-start, if available

mp (rhythm off)

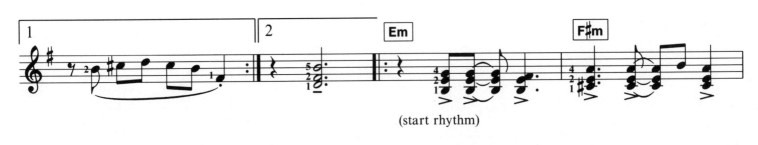

(start rhythm)

* **Downwards Arpeggio.** Play the four notes as rapidly as possible from the top downwards.

CHORD OF E♭ MINOR (E♭m)

3

Using single-finger chord method:

Locate 'E♭' (the higher one) in the accompaniment section of your keyboard. Convert this note into 'E♭m' (see The Complete Keyboard Player, Book Two, p.28, and your owner's manual).

Using fingered chord method:

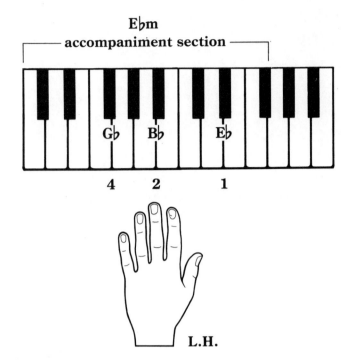

CHORD SEQUENCE PROGRAMMING

4

A useful feature of many modern keyboards (including organs) is that you can record a chord sequence on its own first, then play it back, and play the melody along with it, using right hand only.

In the next piece, 'Never Give Up On A Good Thing', a lively George Benson

number, the timing of the melody is rather complex. It might be a good idea, therefore, to record the chord sequence first, so that you can concentrate fully on your right hand later. Refer to your owner's manual for any special instructions regarding the recording of the chords.

NEVER GIVE UP ON A GOOD THING

Words & Music by T. Shapiro & M. Garvin

Suggested registration: jazz organ + trumpet + tremolo
Rhythm: disco (or rock)
Tempo: medium (♩ = 112)

GIVE ME THE NIGHT

Words & Music by Rod Temperton

Suggested registration: jazz flute + rock guitar
+ chorus (chorale) Duet on (if available)
Rhythm: disco (or rock)
Tempo: medium (♩ = 112)
synchro-start, if available

When ev - er dark is fall___ in' You know the
eve - nin' ac - tion. A place to
stay to - geth___ er. We'll feel the

spir - it of the par - ty starts to come a - live.__ Un - til the day is dawn in',
dine, a glass of wine, a lit - tle late ro - mance, it's just a chain re - ac - tion,
rhy - thm of the eve - ning tak - in' us up high_____ Nev - er mind the weath - er,

you can throw out all the blues and hit the cit - y lights. 'Cause there's
we'll see the people of the world com - in' out to dance. 'Cause there's
we'll be dan - cin' in the street un - til the mor - ning light. 'Cause there's

CHORUS

to Coda ⊕

change guitar to piccolo

mu - sic in the air, and lots of lov - in' ev - 'ry - where, so give me the night.

Give me the night. You need the

KEY OF D (MAJOR)

5 When you are playing in this key you must remember to play all F's and C's, wherever they might fall on the keyboard, as F Sharps and C Sharps, respectively.

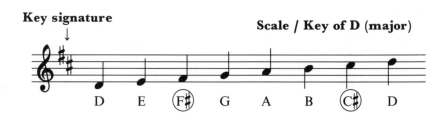

CHORD OF A

6 Using single-finger chord method:

Play the note 'A' in the accompaniment section of your keyboard.

Using fingered chord method:

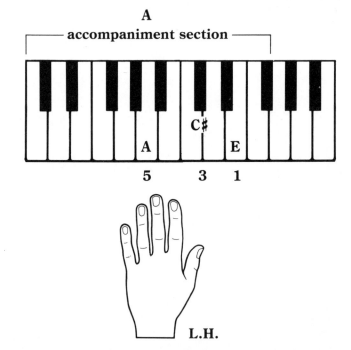

DOUBLE-TRACKING

7 'Breezin'' is the first of the songs in these books to be arranged with a counter melody line (called here a 'Backing Track'), which may be played together with the main melody, using recording techniques.

1. Using the Music Programmer on your keyboard (or a separate tape recorder), record the Melody Track and Chords first (either separately, or together).

2. Play back the recorded Melody Track and play the Backing Track along with it (right hand only).

BREEZIN'

Words & Music by Bobby Womack

Suggested registration: string ensemble
Music programmer: orchestra & chord only (solo off)
Record Melody Track and Chords first
Rhythm: bossa nova
Tempo: quite fast (♩ = 160)

* change strings to jazz guitar
+ half sustain

* Registration changes in double-tracking pieces will be made after the recording, at the playback stage.
Since you will be playing right hand only at this time, you will be able to make the registration changes easily with your left hand.

25

SUSSUDIO

Words & Music by Phil Collins

Suggested registration: brass ensemble
+ piccolo + chorus (chorale)
Rhythm: 16 beat (rock)
Tempo: medium (♩ = 126)
synchro-start, if available

There's a girl that's been on my mind_____
mf I know that I'm too young,_____

all the time_____ sus - sus - sud-i-o.
my life has just be - gun,_____ sus - sus - sud-i-o.
f

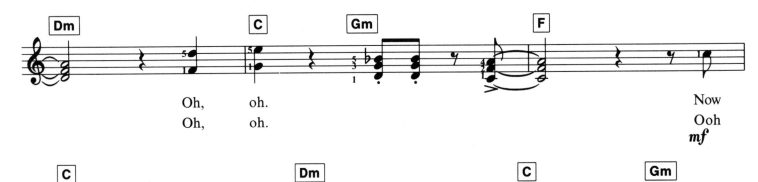

Oh, oh.
Oh, oh. Now
Ooh
mf

she don't ev - en know my name,_____ but I think she likes me just the
give me a chance, give me a sign,_____ I'll show her an - y -

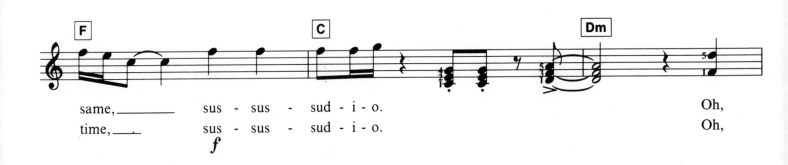

same,_____ sus - sus - sud - i - o. Oh,
time,____ sus - sus - sud - i - o. Oh,
f

LONG LONG WAY TO GO

Words & Music by Phil Collins

Suggested registration: hawaiian guitar (or jazz guitar)
+ medium sustain + chorus (chorale)
Rhythm: 16 beat (rock)
Tempo: medium 2 (♩ = 60)

While   I   sit   here   try-ing to think____   of things to
While   I   sit   here   try-ing to move ____ you an - y - way I
While   we   sit   and we   talk   and talk _____   and talk some

say. ____
can. ____   Some - one   lies   bleed - ing   in   a   field   some -
more. __   Some __ one's   son   lies   dead   in   a
                             Some __ one's   loved   one's   heart   stops

where.   So   you can
gut - ter   some-where.   And it would
beat - ing in   a street   some-where.   So   it would

see   we   still   got   a   long   long ___ way   to   go. ____
seem we've still   got   a   long   long ___ way   to   go. ____
seem we've still   got   a   long   long ___ way   to   go. ____

I've seen   all   I   wan - na   see   to - day.
I   can't   take   it   an - y - more.
I've heard   all   I   wan - na   hear   to - day.

CHORUS

add trumpet

f Turn it off if you want to,____ switch it off it will

go a____ way. Turn it off if you want to.____

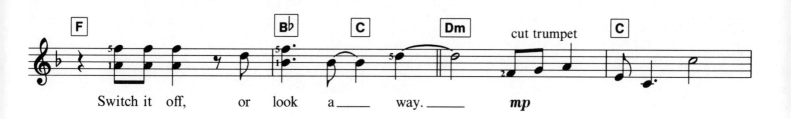

Switch it off, or look a____ way.____ *mp*

to Coda ⊕   *D.C. al Coda*   ⊕ *CODA*

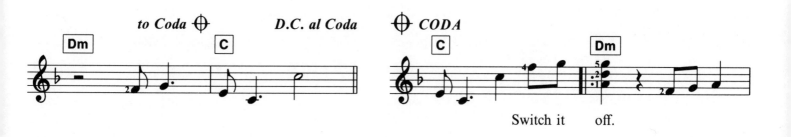

Switch it off.

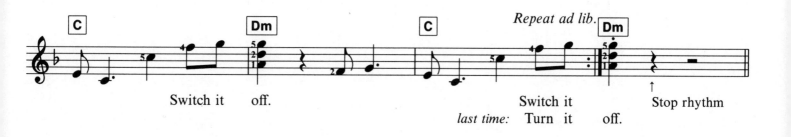

Switch it off.   Switch it   Stop rhythm

last time: Turn it off.

ONE MORE NIGHT

Words & Music by Phil Collins

Suggested registration: string ensemble
Rhythm: rock
Tempo: medium 2 (♩ = 63)

PASSING STRANGERS

Words & Music by J. Ure, B. Currie, W. Cann & C. Allen

Suggested registration: cosmic + chorus (chorale)
Rhythm: rock
Tempo: quite fast (♩ = 144)

8 Using single-finger chord method:

Play the note 'A♭' in the accompaniment section of your keyboard.

Using fingered chord method:

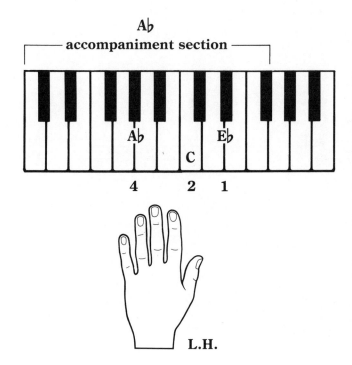

THE VOICE

Words & Music by J. Ure, B. Currie, W. Cann & C. Allen

Suggested registration: jazz flute + violin
+ chorus (chorale)
Rhythm: rock
Tempo: fast (♩ = 160)

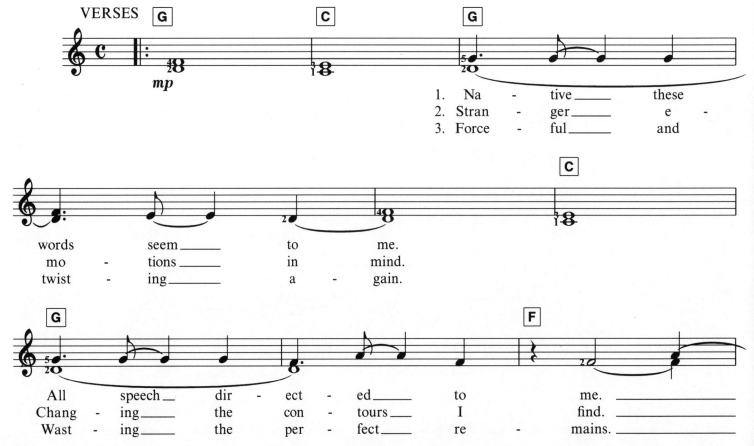

1. Na - tive _____ these words _____ seem _____ to me. All speech _____ dir - ect - ed _____ to me. _____
2. Stran - ger _____ e - mo - tions _____ in mind. Chang - ing _____ the con - tours _____ I find. _____
3. Force - ful _____ and twist - ing _____ a - gain. Wast - ing _____ the per - fect _____ re - mains. _____

VIENNA

Words & Music by J. Ure, B. Currie, W. Cann & C. Allen

Suggested registration:
orchestra: pipe organ with slight sustain
solo: rock guitar with slight sustain
+ chorus (chorale) + duet & variation (if available)
Music programmer: orchestra & chord only (solo off)
Record backing track + chords first
Rhythm: rock
Tempo: slow (♩ = 80)
synchro - start, if available.

HERE COMES THE RAIN AGAIN

Words & Music by A. Lennox & D. A. Stewart

Suggested registration: strings + elec. guitar
+ arpeggio, if available
Rhythm: rock
Tempo: fairly fast (♩ = 132)

VERSES

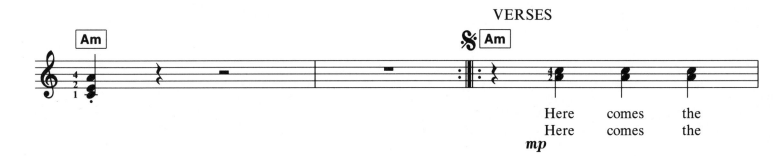

Here comes the
Here comes the

rain a - gain,___ fall - ing on my head like a mem - o - ry,___
rain a - gain,___ rain - ing in my head like a trag - e - dy,___

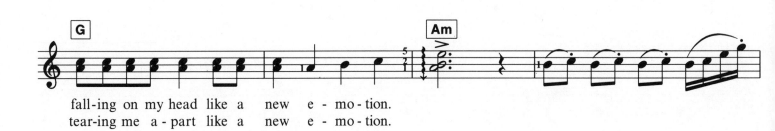

fall - ing on my head like a new e - mo - tion.
tear - ing me a - part like a new e - mo - tion.

F

I want to walk in the o-pen wind, I want to talk like lov-ers do,___
I want to breathe in the o-pen wind, I want to kiss like lov-ers do,___

G
Am
change to organ,
with tremolo

want to dive in-to your o-cean, is it rain-ing___ with you? so ba-by,
want to dive in-to your o-cean, is it rain-ing___ with you?

CHORUS

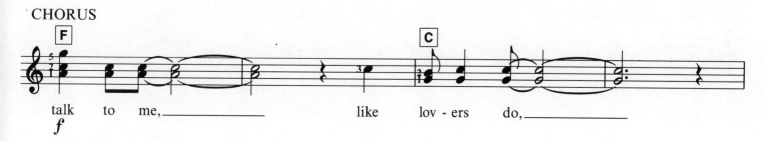

F
C

talk to me,_____ like lov-ers do,_____

f

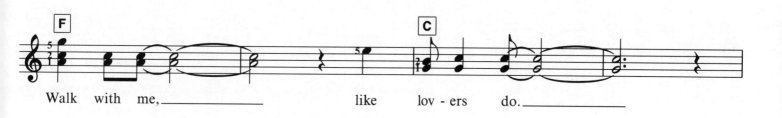

F
C

Walk with me,_____ like lov-ers do._____

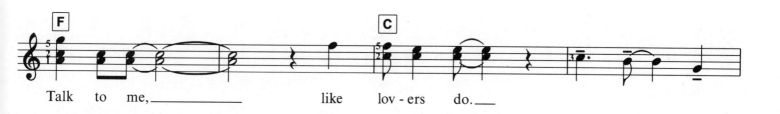

F
C

Talk to me,_____ like lov-ers do.___

D. 𝄋 and FADE
on CHORUS *(2nd time)*
to strings and guitar

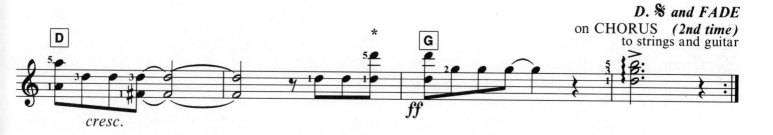

D
*
G

cresc.

ff

* **high D,** if available

WHO'S THAT GIRL?

Words & Music by A. Lennox & D. A. Stewart

Suggested registration: harpsichord, fairly long sustain,
medium tremolo
Rhythm: rock
Tempo: medium (♩ = 120)
synchro-start, if available

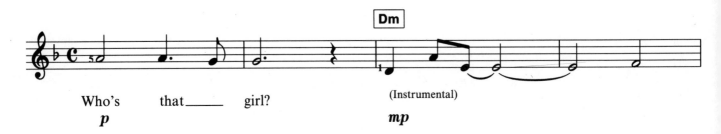

Who's   that___   girl?

p   (Instrumental)   *mp*

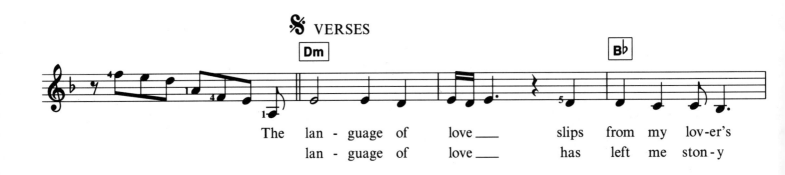

VERSES

The lan - guage of love ___ slips from my lov-er's
lan - guage of love ___ has left me ston - y

tongue.___   Cool - er than ice ___ cream,   and   warm - er than the
grey, ___   tongue tied and twist ___ ed,   at the price I've had to

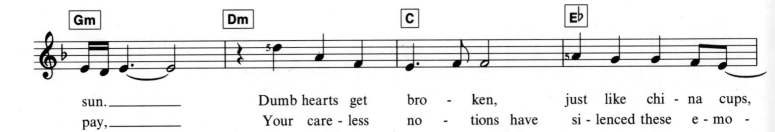

sun._____   Dumb hearts get bro - ken,   just like chi - na cups,
pay,_____   Your care - less no - tions have si - lenced these e - mo -

RIGHT BY YOUR SIDE

Words & Music by A. Lennox & D. A. Stewart

Suggested registration: jazz guitar, with short sustain + piccolo.
Duet & arpeggio, if available. Tremolo.
Music programmer: orchestra & chord only (solo off)
Record Melody Track & Chords first.
Rhythm: rhumba
Tempo: quite fast (♩ = 168)

CHORD CHART

9 (Showing all 'fingered chords' used in The Complete Rock & Pop Keyboard Player).

C
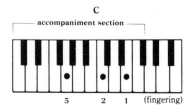

Cm
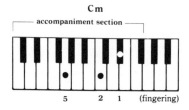

C7
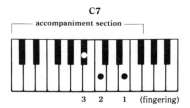

D♭
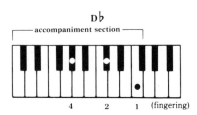

C#m
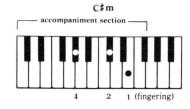

D
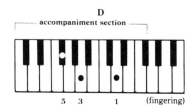

Dm
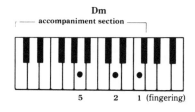

D7
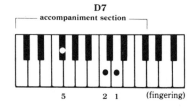

E♭
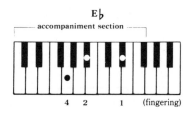

E♭m
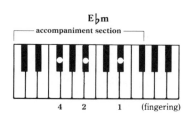

E
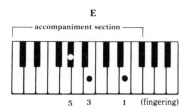

Em
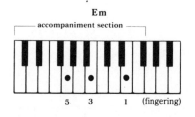

E7
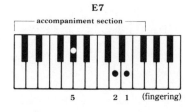

F
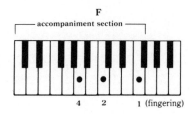

Fm
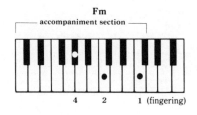

F7
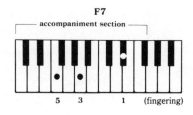

G♭(F#)

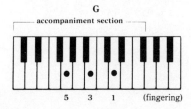

F#m

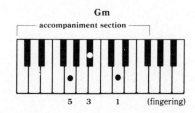

G

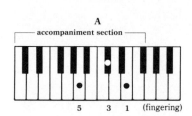

Gm

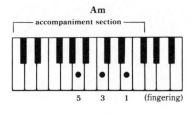

G7

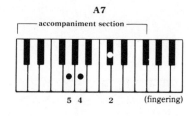

A♭

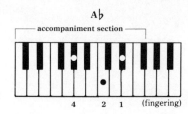

A

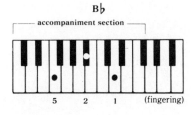

Am

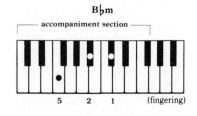

A7

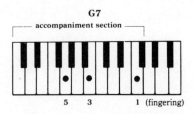

B♭

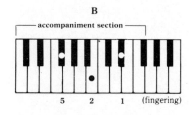

B♭m

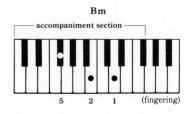

B

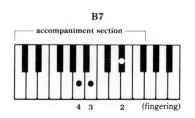

Bm

B7

DISCOGRAPHY

ARTIST	TITLE	ALBUM No
George Benson	The George Benson Collection	Warner Bros K 66107
Chris De Burgh	Into The Light	AMA 5121
Phil Collins	No Jacket Required	Virgin V 2345
Culture Club	Colour By Numbers	Virgin V 2285
Eurythmics	Touch	RCA PL 70109
Ultravox	Vienna	Chrysalis CHR 1296
	Rage In Eden	Chrysalis CHR 1338

10400 7/90